GRADE
5

comparative superlative

singular plural

FLASH FORWARD

Language Arts

figurative persuasive

Written by **Kathy Furgang**

Illustrations by **Christine Schneider**

Cover illustration by John Haslam
Cover design by Loira Walsh
Interior design by Gladys Lai
Production by Design Lab NYC, Inc.
Edited by Hilda Diaz

Flash Kids
A Division of Barnes & Noble
122 Fifth Avenue
New York, NY 10011

ISBN: 978-1-4114-2733-4

Please submit all inquiries to FlashKids@bn.com

Printed and bound in the United States

1 3 5 7 9 10 8 6 4 2

Communication, both written and oral, is vital to success in school.

Language Arts encompasses these essential skills. Through almost 100 pages of entertaining language exercises for fifth-graders, this workbook covers important topics such as reading comprehension, phonics, grammar, vocabulary, writing, and speaking.

Flash Forward Language Arts features mazes, puzzles, and activities designed to help your student develop grammar, spelling, and writing skills. Your student will learn to draw inferences and generalizations, identify plot and theme, and understand literary devices such as metaphors. This workbook also includes plenty of creative writing exercises and practice in numerous test-taking formats, including multiple-choice and open-ended questions.

The activities in this workbook are designed for your student to handle alone, but your assistance and interaction can greatly enhance the learning experience. As you work through the activities together, challenge your student to stretch his or her skills. Remember, however, that some concepts here will be new and require patience to master. Offer your student plenty of praise and support. After the completion of each page, you can check the answers at the back of the workbook. Use incorrect answers as an opportunity to review and rework.

In addition to working together on the pages of this book, you can encourage language skills through everyday activities. Here are some simple, age-appropriate ways to incorporate writing and oral skills into daily life. Ask your student to:

- Compare and contrast two characters from a favorite book
- Recount the plot of a television show or movie
- Give step-by-step directions for playing a game, creating a craft, or cooking a simple recipe
- Write a poem using figurative language
- Compose a persuasive essay on a topic of personal importance
- Use context clues to identify unknown words in everyday reading

These and dozens of other activities are excellent ways to help your student develop essential communications skills. Remember, language is everywhere!

Prefixes

A **prefix** is a word part that appears before a root word or a base word.

For example: The prefix *un-* means *not.* So the word *unmade* means *not made.*

Complete the word in each sentence. Circle the correct prefix in parentheses.

1. Shawna looked at her test paper in ___belief. (dis- / un- / ex-)

2. She hoped the teacher would ___calculate her score. (de- / re- / dis-)

3. The essay that she wrote was ___fiction. (un- / non- / ex-)

4. Her ___action to the grade was strong. (non- / ex- / re-)

5. Shawna wished she could just ___form the paper into a perfect A.
(re- / trans- / non-)

Match each word with its meaning. Write the letter on the line.

6. ___ unhealthy   **a.** to use caution before

7. ___ redo   **b.** to do again

8. ___ precaution   **c.** not healthy

9. ___ depart   **d.** to leave

Suffixes

A **suffix** is a word part that appears after a root word or a base word.

For example: The suffix -er means *one who.* So, the word *teacher* means *one who teaches.*

Complete the word in each sentence. Circle the correct suffix in parentheses.

1. We cannot believe how care_____ Leah is being with the flowers.
(-able / -ful / -ish)

2. Babies are usual_____ so rough when they handle things. (-ly / -ible / -or)

3. I did not expect her to show kind_____ when she touched the flower.
(-ment / -ness / -er)

4. Leah is such a love_____ baby! (-ish / -able / -ful)

5. Even so, get that flower away from her quick_____! (-ful / -ness / -ly)

Match each word with its meaning. Write the letter on the line.

6. ___ believable   **a.** one who acts

7. ___ possibly   **b.** able to be believed

8. ___ creative   **c.** full of health

9. ___ actor   **d.** it is possible

10. ___ healthful   **e.** able to create

Capitals Everywhere

There are several places where **capital letters** must be used. The names of people and places, days of the week, and months of the year should always be capitalized. The beginning of a sentence must also always be capitalized.

For example:

We can go to the restaurant in *Madison Park* on *Tuesday*. *They* have great *Italian* food. *Call Jackie* to meet us there.

Rewrite each sentence using correct capitalization.

1. my little sister, lanie, loves superheroes like batman and spiderman.

_____

2. she bought a superhero coloring book when we visited san diego, california.

_____

3. we were there for thanksgiving last year and walked along main street.

_____

4. lanie pointed and cheered at every superhero poster outside lowland theaters.

_____

5. mom and dad bought her a green lantern action figure.

_____

6. they gave it to her for her birthday in december.

_____

7. when she opened it, she thought it was the best gift in the world!

_____

What Is the Tense?

A verb's **tense** tells the time in which the action takes place. In the past tense, the action has already taken place. In the present tense, the action is taking place now. In the future tense, the action has not yet taken place.

For example:

Past tense	The horse *galloped* through the field.
Present tense	The horse *gallops* through the field.
Future tense	The horse *will gallop* through the field.

Which tense is each sentence written in? Write *past, present,* or *future.*

1. Jessie plays at the school playground every day. _____

2. He will even go out there in the snow. _____

3. The cold weather will not bother him. _____

4. My dog is eating his meal in the kitchen. _____

5. I served him breakfast at eight this morning. _____

6. He leaves the food that he cannot finish. _____

7. Aaron played the violin at the concert. _____

8. The audience will cheer when he finishes. _____

9. I took violin lessons after school. _____

10. I learned a lot from my teacher. _____

So Many Synonyms

> A **synonym** is a word that means the same or almost the same as another word.
>
> For example:
>   The word *infant* is a synonym for *baby*.
>   The word *summit* is a synonym for *peak*.

Replace the underlined word in each sentence with its synonym.
Circle the correct word in parentheses.

1. The swim coach wore the team jersey to school today. (shirt / sweater)

2. We are not allowed to complain about the new practice schedule.
(protest / talk)

3. The swimmers were exhausted after winning their first meet.
(tired / hungry)

4. The team has devoted fans who will cheer whether they win or lose.
(trusting / loyal)

5. We have a chance to win a massive trophy at the end of the season.
(giant / powerful)

6. The president made an interesting comment in her speech. (joke / remark)

7. He called a meeting of many important people. (conference / party)

8. Wild applause could be heard from the audience. (fierce / funny)

9. The people will discuss federal issues. (national / important)

Opposite Antonyms

An **antonym** is a word that means the opposite of another word.

For example:
The word *forward* is an antonym for *backward*.
The word *strong* is an antonym for *frail*.

Replace the underlined word in each sentence with its antonym.
Circle the correct word in parentheses.

1. I gave a <u>dynamic</u> report in school today. (boring / short)

2. I included a <u>fancy</u> chart about the topic. (terrible / plain)

3. The teacher said it should be a <u>formal</u> report. (casual / loud)

4. I was <u>thrilled</u> with the teacher's reaction.
(upset / late)

5. The class was <u>alert</u> when I gave the report.
(inattentive / impolite)

6. Look at the dog. She's <u>filthy</u>! (clean / dirty)

7. Let's clean her before our guests <u>arrive</u>. (come / leave)

8. I get <u>discouraged</u> when I have to wrestle with the dog to get her to bathe.
(angry / encouraged)

9. Why does she <u>detest</u> the tub so much? (love / fear)

10. I wish I could teach her to be more <u>patient</u>. (calm / impatient)

What's Fact? What's Opinion?

A **fact** is a statement that is true and can be proven. An **opinion** is what someone thinks or feels. An opinion cannot be proven.

For example:

Fact   Mrs. Lee is a teacher.
Opinion   Mrs. Lee is the best teacher in the world.

Read the story. Then circle *fact* or *opinion* for each related sentence below.

Mustaf was very hungry when he walked into the cafeteria. He looked at the choices behind the counter. There was baked macaroni, pizza, hamburgers, chicken noodle soup, and salad. "Wow, pizza!" Mustaf thought. Mustaf couldn't believe anyone would want any of the other choices when there was pizza available. The more pizza, the better!

1. When Mustaf walked into the cafeteria, he was very hungry.

fact   opinion

2. He looked around at the choices behind the counter.

fact   opinion

3. Mustaf could choose from baked macaroni, pizza, hamburgers, chicken noodle soup, and salad.

fact   opinion

4. Pizza makes everyone think, "Wow!"

fact   opinion

5. Who would want any of the other choices when there is pizza available!

fact   opinion

6. The more pizza, the better.

fact   opinion

Good Description!

Descriptive writing gives details about something. Descriptions make writing more exact.

For example:

There are many ways to describe a vase. Is it tall or short? What color is it? Does it have a design on it? How big is it?

Look around the room you are in. Choose any object you want and write a detailed description of it.

The Right Root

A **root word** is the smaller, meaningful word that makes up part of a longer word. A prefix, suffix, or both word parts are added to a root to make a new, related word.

For example:
The root word of *dishearten* is *heart*.
The root word of *magician* is *magic*.

Look at each word. Write the root word.

1. communication _____

2. foundation _____

3. exchanging _____

4. illustration _____

5. reintroduction _____

6. cowardly _____

7. undisturbed _____

8. approval _____

9. assistance _____

10. economic _____

11. unintelligently _____

12. similarity _____

13. responsibility _____

14. seriously _____

Same or Different?

Remember: **Synonyms** are words that have the same meaning.
Antonyms are words that have opposite meanings.

Match each word to a synonym. Write the letter on the line.

1. ___ trust

2. ___ commotion

3. ___ innovative

4. ___ intelligent

5. ___ anger

a. knowledgeable

b. advanced

c. confidence

d. rage

e. disturbance

Match each word to an antonym. Write the letter on the line.

6. ___ peace

7. ___ happiness

8. ___ partial

9. ___ energized

10. ___ honest

f. deceptive

g. complete

h. war

i. despair

j. tired

One or Many?

A **singular noun** names one person, place, or thing.
A **plural noun** names more than one person, place, or thing.

For example:
    Singular nouns dog, friend, Aunt Mary, Elm Street
    Plural nouns   hats, bicycles, soldiers, parks

Read each sentence. Underline the singular nouns. Circle the plural nouns.

1. We left our toothbrushes on the sink and put on our pajamas.

2. My dog ate cookies and biscuits off the floor.

3. The students put their backpacks on the floor and hung up their coats.

4. I saw so many fish in the ocean today!

Read each sentence. If the underlined noun is singular, rewrite the sentence so the noun is plural. If the underlined noun is plural, rewrite the sentence so the noun is singular.

5. I returned my <u>book</u> to the library today.

_____

6. We ran through the <u>street</u> as quickly as we could.

_____

7. I met my <u>classmates</u> on the playground today.

_____

8. Mom saw the <u>snowman</u> we made in the yard.

_____

Who Does It Belong To?

A **singular possessive noun** is one that uses an apostrophe plus *s* to show who owns something.

For example:
- The friend of the boy = the boy's friend
- The bottle of the baby = baby's bottle
- The pages of the book = the book's pages
- The hat of Mom = Mom's hat

Rewrite each sentence to make the underlined part into a singular possessive noun.

1. <u>The bone of the dog</u> is in the backyard.

_____

2. <u>The brother of Sue</u> is at the door.

_____

3. <u>The blanket of the dog</u> is in the dryer.

_____

4. <u>The color of the house</u> is blue.

_____

5. <u>The friend of Samantha</u> is sick today.

_____

6. <u>The necklace of Jenny</u> is beautiful.

_____

7. <u>The nest of the bird</u> was hidden in the branches.

_____

She Agrees, They Agree

Subject-verb agreement is when the subject of a sentence agrees in number with the verb of a sentence. A plural subject such as *we* and *they* must use a plural verb, such as *talk*. A singular subject such as *she* or *he* must use a singular verb, such as *talks*.

Complete each sentence. Circle the correct form of each verb in parentheses to agree with the subject.

1. Donny and Abigail (sing / sings) the national anthem.

2. The cat (run / runs) under the couch.

3. The neighbors (join / joins) in also.

4. The kids (love / loves) to sing and dance together.

5. We (try / tries) to help them sing another song.

Complete each sentence. Circle the correct subject in parentheses to agree with the verb.

6. The (boy / boys) wrestle with the dog.

7. My (dog / dogs) wins every wrestling match.

8. (He / They) gobbles up food from his dog bowl every day at noon.

9. The (boy / boys) guarantee a big win in today's wrestling match.

10. I (know / knows) Bronco the dog will prevail!

How Will It End?

Stories have a beginning, a middle, and an end. A story **ending** wraps up the events of the story and solves the problem, or conflict.

Write an ending for the story beginning below.

Liam could see the storm in the distance. He rushed the cows and horses into the barn and closed the door as quickly as he could. The animals sensed the approaching storm and were frightened. Liam looked around the barn. There was not much he could do now except wait for the storm to pass.

_____

_____

_____

_____

_____

_____

_____

_____

_____

What a Character!

A **character** is a person or animal in a story. Characters help tell a story. You can describe the way a character looks, acts, and feels.

For example:

The Big Bad Wolf is a character that helps tell the story of "The Three Little Pigs." You can describe the wolf as mean, dangerous, and scary-looking!

Think of a character you know from a story. Write a description of the character. Include as many details as possible to describe the character.

_____

_____

_____

_____

_____

_____

_____

_____

Fact vs. Opinion

Remember: A **fact** is a statement that is true and can be proven.
An **opinion** is the way someone thinks or feels. An opinion cannot be proven.

Read the passage below. Then list the facts and opinions.

The elephant is one of the most interesting animals in the world. When people think of the elephant, they often wish they could learn more about it. The animal's best feature is its trunk. The elephant uses its trunk to tear branches from trees and then place them into its mouth to eat. The trunk is used for drinking, too. Elephants suck water into their trunks and then blow it into their mouths to drink! The trunk is even used to greet other elephants. Many people think that two elephants greeting each other with their trunks looks a little like two people shaking hands.

FACTS	**OPINIONS**
_____	_____
_____	_____
_____	_____
_____	_____
_____	_____
_____	_____

What's the Big Idea?

The **main idea** of a passage tells what the passage is mainly about. The **supporting details** of a passage give information to support the main idea. Supporting details are less important than the main idea and could not stand by themselves in a passage.

For example:

Main idea: Three Little Pigs try to stay safe from the Big Bad Wolf. They stay safe in a house made of bricks.

Supporting details: One pig makes his house out of straw, and the other makes his house out of twigs.

Read the passage below, then write the main idea, and list the supporting details.

Jake was the best baseball player on his team. He dreamed of being a professional baseball player since he was three years old and his dad brought him to a game in a big stadium. He couldn't believe the huge field, the big lights, and the excited fans. From that day on, Jake practiced throwing, catching, and hitting a baseball every single day. At first he did not do so well, but slowly he began to get better and better. Soon he was old enough to join a team. By then he was already better than most players his age ever dreamed they could be. Jake was already on his way to his big dream!

Main idea

_____

_____

_____

Supporting details

_____

_____

_____

Perfect Prefixes

Remember: A **prefix** is a word part that appears before a root or base word.

Read each sentence. Find the word that uses a prefix.
Circle the prefix and write another sentence that uses the same word.

1. Kavita felt a bit unbalanced on her new bike.

_____

2. Dad said that my answer about where I was last night was nonsense.

_____

3. I hope you do not misunderstand my letter.

_____

4. I wanted to reassure you that you are still a great athlete.

_____

Write a word with a prefix that means the same as the words shown.

5. not believable _____

6. view before _____

7. after season _____

8. not important_____

9. live through again _____

Super Suffixes

Remember: A **suffix** is a word part that appears after a root or base word.

Read each sentence. Find the word that uses a suffix.
Circle the suffix and write another sentence that uses the same word.

1. I saw such a wonderful concert last night.

_____

2. The conductor of the children's choir did a great job.

_____

3. The kids gave a recital that would brighten anyone's day.

_____

4. We all left the concert hall sincerely happy about the experience.

_____

Write the word with a suffix that means the same as the words shown.

5. result of placing _____

6. person who studies science _____

7. full of fear _____

8. having no fear _____

9. in a quick way _____

You Can Quote Me!

Quotation marks tell the reader when a character begins and stops speaking. The first word in a quotation is capitalized, and quotations are set off by commas within sentences.

For example:
"I think I left my backpack on the bus," said Norman.

Rewrite the paragraph below using quotation marks correctly.

Hurry up said Dad. The bus is going to be here any minute!

OK, I yelled back. I quickly looked around the room. I could not find my backpack anywhere. I'll be there in a minute! I said.

What's taking you so long? Dad said, standing in the doorway with my backpack in his hands. It looks like you lost something.

Dad! I said. I was looking for that! Thanks.

_____

_____

_____

_____

_____

_____

_____

Don't Be Too Negative!

Words like *no, not, nobody, nowhere, never,* and *nothing* are **negative** words. A **double negative** means that two negatives are used in the same sentence. Avoid double negatives. They change the meaning of the sentence to have a positive meaning.

Rewrite the sentences to eliminate double negatives.
Keep only the first negative in each sentence.

1. Jerry does not think nobody will come to his party.

_____

2. He doesn't have no friends.

_____

3. He hasn't not lived in town for a very long time.

_____

4. His mom told him he couldn't invite nobody who was a stranger.

_____

5. Jerry can't never wait for a birthday, even if very few people come to his party.

_____

6. Nobody makes no cake better than Aunt Carmen.

_____

7. Jerry doesn't have nothing to worry about.

_____

Lovely, Descriptive Adjectives

An **adjective** is a word that describes a noun. Adjectives describe feel, taste, smell, color, size, or number. Adjectives help describe things and give the reader a better picture.

For example:
The *cold, wet* snow fell on the *brown* rooftop.
Abby bought a *gorgeous* dress yesterday.

Complete each sentence. Use the adjectives in the word bank.

furry	twelve	remarkable	difficult
huge	soft	adorable	yellow	hilarious

1. Wanda put the _____ banana on the counter.

2. My friends made a _____ mural that takes up the whole side of the school.

3. We made a _____ science project that dazzled the whole school.

4. Gabriela's cat has a _____ coat that makes me sneeze.

5. My mother bought _____ eggs so that she would have a dozen.

6. Zack's joke was _____ and kept everyone laughing.

7. Mike thought he did poorly on the test because many of the questions were too _____.

8. As the strawberries ripened, they began to get _____.

9. Everyone thought the baby was _____ because she could wave bye-bye.

Contraction Action

A **contraction** is a combination of two words. An apostrophe takes the place of a missing letter in the contraction.

For example:
they would = they'd	I will = I'll
is not = isn't	should not = shouldn't
we have = we've	she had = she'd

Rewrite the underlined part of each sentence as a contraction.

1. <u>They will</u> be at the hockey game early today. _____

2. <u>We had</u> better get going so that we will not be late. _____

3. The coach <u>could not</u> call everyone to cancel the practice. _____

4. My friends <u>are not</u> going to be at the game tomorrow. _____

5. You <u>should not</u> practice after it gets dark. _____

6. <u>I will</u> look at the weather report for tomorrow's game. _____

7. <u>It has</u> been rainy every day this week. _____

8. <u>We will</u> practice at Tommy's house next time. _____

9. <u>He had</u> better tell us if the game is canceled. _____

10. <u>We are</u> going to wait for his call. _____

In the Beginning

The **beginning** of a story introduces characters and events.
It may also talk about the story's conflict, or problem, for the first time.

Write a beginning for the story ending below.

_____

_____

_____

_____

_____

_____

_____

_____

_____

The squirrels could not believe their eyes! When they climbed up to their nest that morning, they found a pile of acorns there. Mama Squirrel smiled. She knew where it had come from.

"I guess we'll have a good winter after all," she sighed, holding her baby squirrels closer to her side.

My Friendly Letter

A **friendly letter** has an opening and a closing. An opening tells who the letter is to and the closing tells who the letter is from. A friendly letter can use informal language, but it should use complete sentences.

Write a friendly letter to someone you know. Tell the person what you did today. Use complete sentences and include an opening and closing.

_____

_____

_____

_____

_____

Name That Genre

A **genre** is a category of writing. There are many genres of literature, such as poetry, fairy tale, play, science fiction, legend, fantasy, and many more.

Read the story and answer the questions below.

Lori took out her cell phone and dialed Mom at the space station. She picked up in a flash. "I'll be home late for dinner tonight," she told Mom.

"But I'm ordering pizza to be delivered from the space station," she said. "Who will be there to pay for it?"

"Can't you just put the house on autopilot?" Lori asked. "It's garbage night too, but I am too busy at space training school to push the garbage button. Just get the house to do it all without us."

Mom agreed to the plan and put the house on autopilot. When they returned late that night, however, they caught the house feeding the pizza to the dog!

1. What is the genre of this story? _____

2. What are the characteristics of the genre?

_____

_____

3. What are some examples from the story that helped you decide on the genre?

_____

_____

_____

How Did You Do That?

How-to writing explains how to do something. It often gives step-by-step instructions so that the reader can repeat them. Look for words such as *first, next,* and *then* to help you follow the steps of the process.

Answer the questions about the recipe below.

This is a great recipe for a healthy and delicious tuna sandwich.

- First, toast two pieces of whole wheat bread.
- Open a six-ounce can of tuna and drain the water.
- Place the tuna in a bowl next and add a small amount of low-fat mayonnaise. Mix well with a fork as you break up the tuna. Mix in small pieces of celery if desired.
- Place the tuna on one slice of the toasted bread. Add your favorite toppings.
- Then add the second slice of bread and cut the sandwich in half.

1. When making the sandwich, what should you do right after you open the can of tuna?

_____

2. How much tuna does the recipe call for?

_____

3. What should be mixed in the bowl with the tuna?

_____

4. What is the last thing you should do to the sandwich before eating it?

_____

Perfect Punctuation

Punctuation marks help to make sentences clear and to separate different parts of a sentence. Periods, commas, question marks, exclamation marks, quotation marks, and parentheses are all kinds of punctuation.

Rewrite each sentence using correct punctuation.

1. Who has a better teacher Alex or Alyssa!

_____

2. That's not a fair question, said Marcus. "People like teachers for different reasons," he said?

_____

3. "I know the answer! said Alyssa. "I definitely have the better, teacher because we hardly. get any homework at all."

_____

4. Well I think my teacher is better," said Alex? "She might give us a lot of homework, but we all learn a lot from her every day"

_____

5. Only one of the teachers gives homework in social studies math English and science every night.

_____

6. Does that make her a good teacher or a bad teacher.

_____

Who Does It Belong To?

A **possessive pronoun** tells who owns something. The most common ones are *my, your, our, their, his, her,* and *its.*

Rewrite each sentence to make the underlined part
a possessive pronoun.

1. The best essay in the class was <u>Maria's</u>.

_____

2. The teacher read the essay that was <u>the one that belongs to you and me</u>.

_____

3. I cannot understand the essay that is <u>the one that belongs to you</u>.

_____

4. Do you like the essay that is <u>the one that belongs to me</u>?

_____

Complete each sentence. Circle the correct pronoun in parentheses.

5. _____ mother wants me to make dinner tonight. (My / Its)

6. _____ dinner tonight will be chicken with a salad. (Our / Ours)

7. I should work harder at _____ music lessons. (mine / my)

Commas Here and There

Correct each sentence. Place commas where they belong.

1. I love it when the winter sky gets cold gray and cloudy.

2. It has been snowing all day and soon I will be able to make a snowman.

3. First I check for clothes that I can wear outside in the snow.

4. I find a hat mittens a scarf boots and a coat.

5. Next I eat a good lunch so I have the energy to make my snowman.

6. I gather snow pack it and roll it across the yard.

7. Suddenly I get a little discouraged because I realize I cannot lift the snowballs.

8. That's when Dad comes out and he is ready to help me.

9. I am happy that he helps but then he makes me help clear snow off the car driveway stairs and walkway.

10. As I shovel my snowman watches me and I think he may have winked at me!

Plural Possessive Practice

A **plural possessive noun** shows the ownership of something by more than one person or thing. For nouns that do not end in *s,* add an apostrophe and *s.* For nouns that end in *s,* just add an apostrophe.

For example:

I will bring the <u>treats of the dogs</u>.   I will bring the dogs' treats.

I will make the <u>meals of the people</u>.   I will make the people's meals.

Rewrite each sentence to make the underlined part a plural possessive noun.

1. We will hand out the <u>uniforms of the athletes</u>.

_____

2. I will keep track of the <u>points of both teams</u>.

_____

3. The <u>tips of the coaches</u> help the teams do well.

_____

4. The <u>efforts of the children</u> are outstanding.

_____

5. I can hear the <u>cheers of the fans</u>!

_____

6. May I see the <u>homes of the animals</u>?

_____

7. The farmers brought us to the <u>nests of the chicken</u>.

_____

What's the Word I'm Looking For?

Remember that **synonyms** are words that have the same meaning, and **antonyms** are words that have the opposite meaning.

Write a synonym and an antonym for each word in the chart below.

	synonym	antonym
1. exquisite		
2. enlarge		
3. sprint		
4. revolt		
5. protect		
6. drowsy		
7. swiftly		
8. fetch		
9. severe		
10. assist		

Get a Clue

A **context clue** is a hint that helps the reader figure out
the meaning of an unknown word. Context clues can give a **definition** or an
example of the unknown word. The clues are sometimes set off in commas.

For example:

      Context definition We will <u>defeat</u>, or *beat,* the other team!

      Context example After the game I felt <u>fatigued</u>. *I was out of breath.*

Look at the underlined word in each sentence. Use the context
clues to help define the word. Then write the meaning of the word.

1. I helped to clean the <u>debris</u>, or garbage, off the beach.

_____

2. A friend should not <u>betray</u> you by telling lies or being mean.

_____

3. I really <u>admire</u>, or respect, my mom for all of the hard work she does.

_____

4. Ellen is a <u>novice</u> at baseball. She didn't even know the rules yet!

_____

Circle the context clue for each underlined word.
Then write whether the context clue is a definition or an example.

5. Matthew has been an <u>orphan</u> since his parents died when he was three.

_____

6. Our teacher <u>insists</u>, or demands, that we do our homework on time.

_____

7. There had been many rabbits eating in the garden, so the carrots were <u>scarce</u>.

_____

Make a Word

Remember: Words are made of parts such as **prefixes**, **roots**, and **suffixes**.
Some words are made of all three word parts!

Prefix	Root word	Suffix
im-	view	-ly
mis-	happy	-ness
un-	proper	-ing
pre-	lead	
	patient	

Read each definition. Choose a word part from each box above to make a new word.

1. a state of not being happy _____

2. the act of leading incorrectly _____

3. in a manner that is not patient _____

4. in a manner that is not proper _____

5. the act of viewing something ahead of time _____

Look at each word. Write the meaning of the underlined word part.

6. inven<u>tor</u> _____

7. excite<u>ment</u> _____

8. <u>tri</u>cycle _____

9. <u>un</u>eventful _____

10. <u>pre</u>caution _____

Go Figure!

Figurative language can help make writing interesting. A **simile** is a figure of speech that uses the words *like* or *as* to compare things. A **metaphor** is a figure of speech that compares things without using *like* or *as*.

For example:

Simile You are as lucky as a four-leaf clover.

Metaphor It's raining cats and dogs.

Read each sentence. Circle *simile* or *metaphor* to identify the figure of speech.

1. Amy became red as a beet when she gave her speech to the class.

simile   metaphor

2. The director always tells us that the world's a stage.

simile   metaphor

3. Mom tells us that friends are golden.

simile   metaphor

4. Ben thought the math test was easy as pie.

simile   metaphor

5. As soon as summer vacation comes, you'll be free as a bird.

simile   metaphor

6. There are times when Gregory walks like a bull in a china shop.

simile   metaphor

7. Juliette's jokes always make her seem as smart as a whip.

simile   metaphor

The Big Idea

Remember: When reading a nonfiction passage, look for the **main idea** and **supporting details**. The main idea tells what the passage is mostly about. The supporting details help tell about the main idea.

Read the passage. Then write the main idea and list the supporting details.

Have you ever heard of a hobbyhorse? It looks a little like an early bicycle, except that you walk with it instead of riding on it. A man named Baron von Drais invented it in 1817. The device had two wheels and was made entirely out of wood. The hobbyhorse became popular for a while during the 1800s, but it was not very useful. It could only be used for walking through a path or garden. You had to wheel it along with you as you walked, but you could lean or sit on it when you needed a rest.

Main idea

_____

_____

Supporting details

_____

_____

_____

_____

_____

Comparing and Contrasting

When you **compare** two things, you tell how they are alike. When you **contrast** two things, you tell how they are different. Comparing and contrasting is an important skill when reading. A Venn diagram can help you keep track of what you compare and contrast as you read.

Fill in the Venn diagram comparing and contrasting the girls based on the passage below.

My friend Sara is a lot like me. We are both in the same grade and we are both on the swim team. We work hard to get our homework done before swim practice so that we can play around and talk on the bus on the way home. But I'm different from Sara, too. I have long brown hair, and she has short blond hair. We like to watch different TV shows. I like to watch comedies and she likes to watch dramas.

Me   **Sara**

Both

Conclusion Solution

When you **draw conclusions** about what you read, you use what you know to figure something out.

For example:
The children stood proudly in front of the class. They smiled and then took their seats as the other children clapped.
Conclusion: The students must have done something good in front of the class.

Draw conclusions from the following passage to answer the questions below.

Danielle had only one more weekend to make the money she needed to buy her parents an anniversary gift. Danielle thought that their neighbor Mrs. Donnelley would definitely hire her. She had a big yard with a lot of trees, and she was very busy. She might really need Danielle's help. Danielle crunched through the leaves on the walkway, rang Mrs. Donnelley's doorbell, and kept her fingers crossed.

1. What do you think Danielle is going to ask Mrs. Donnelley?

_____

_____

2. What tools does Danielle need to have to earn her money?

_____

3. What clues helped you draw a conclusion about what Danielle was doing?

_____

_____

_____

Is It a Cause. . .or an Effect?

A **cause** is the reason that something happens. An **effect** is what happens as a result. When you read, look for cause-and-effect relationships.

For example:
> **Cause** The weather reporter warned that a hurricane was coming.
> **Effect** We packed up our bags and evacuated to Grandma's house!

The weather reports had been given for days already. Most people do not want to stick around town when a hurricane is coming. We were used to these storms because we live near the ocean. Dad and I boarded up the house again. We keep extra boards in the garage for times just like this. I'm getting good at nailing them up, too. While we do this job, Mom and Emily pack up our clothes and food and put them in the car. We have a strong house, so we are confident that everything will be OK while we are gone. And besides, it is always fun to go to Grandma's house.

Fill in the chart with causes and effects from the passage.

Cause	Effect
1. The weather report is given.	
2.	Dad and I board up the house.
3. We have a strong house.	

What's the Order?

When writing about events or steps in a process, it helps to write information in order. Record what happened **first**, **next**, and **last**. This will make your writing more organized and easier to understand.

For example: **First** Sparkles stretched her paws and yawned.
Next She peeked out the front window.
Last She scratched at the windowpane and meowed loudly.

Use the chart below to tell about an event that happened to you.
Then write about it in an interesting way.

First	**Next**	**Last**

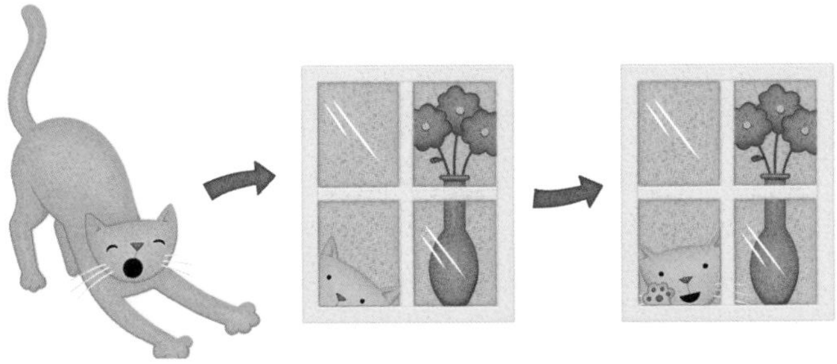

What's the Big Idea?

When you **research** nonfiction topics, it helps to record the main idea and details before you begin writing. A graphic organizer can help you record information.

For example:

life cycle

growth rate

bananas

ecosystem

nutrition

uses

Use the graphic organizer to write the main idea and details about a topic of your choice. Then write the information in the form of an essay.

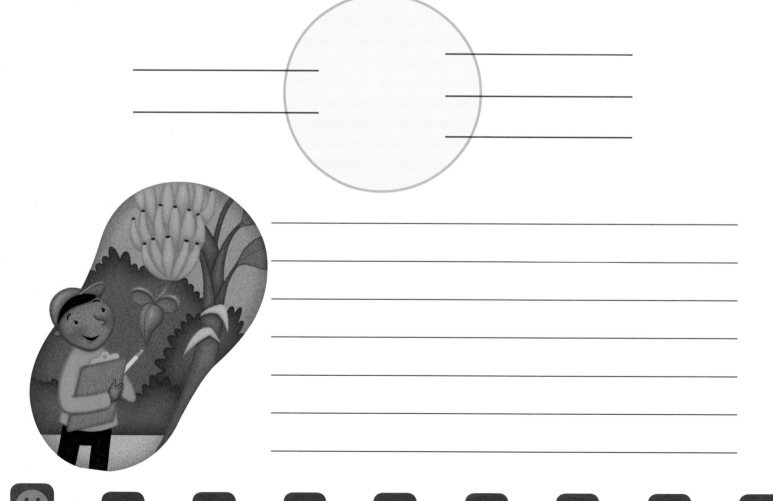

And Then What Happened?

Remember: A good story has a beginning, a middle, and an end. A story ending is a **conclusion** that solves the problem, or conflict, of the story.

Write a conclusion that will solve the problem, or conflict, to the story below.

Arthur rowed the boat as far as his arms would allow. He knew that his brother was hurt and could not do his share of rowing. He hoped his parents were back at the cabin when they arrived at the dock. They might be able to hear his calls for help from there. As he rowed closer and closer to the dock, he crossed his fingers and hoped for the best.

_____

_____

_____

_____

_____

_____

_____

We Need the Word *Be*

The verb *be* has several forms. The words *is, are,* and *am* are used as present-tense forms of the verb *be*. The words *was* and *were* are the past-tense forms.

Complete each sentence. Use the correct past-tense form of *be*.

1. The soccer game _____ canceled today because of the rain.

2. The kids _____ upset that they could not play in the semifinals.

3. We _____ going to reschedule the game for tomorrow.

4. But the coaches _____ not able to reschedule until next week.

5. The whole team _____ disappointed.

Complete each sentence. Use the correct present-tense form of *be*.

6. We _____ having a test this week about Africa.

7. Sasha _____ just about as ready for the test as I _____.

8. The class _____ studying a little bit together.

9. Then we _____ dividing into small groups to reread our books.

10. I think I _____ going to do fine as long as I work hard!

Independent or Dependent?

An **independent clause** is a group of words with a subject and verb that makes a complete thought. A **dependent clause** is a group of words with a subject and verb that does not make a complete thought and must be connected to another part of a sentence in order to make sense.

Read each clause. Write *dependent* or *independent*.

1. Jake disappointed the coach by not showing up to the final game. _____

2. The team could not wait until summer. _____

3. When they looked at the field in disbelief._____

4. Seeing how happy everyone was after they won the game. _____

5. Jake wished he could have been there with his friends and teammates.

_____

6. Coach smiled out of the corner of his mouth. _____

7. Roared the crowd! _____

8. It was the team's very best game, so coach's initial disappointment disappeared.

_____

9. When they are all proud to be part of the team. _____

Is That Right, or Is that Write?

A **homophone** is a pair or group of words that sound the same but have different meanings and spellings. The correct homophone must be used for a sentence to make sense.

For example:
 I had a *great* time last night.
 Don't forget to *grate* the cheese!

Read each sentence. Circle the word that is an incorrect homophone.
Write the correct homophone on the line.

1. Animals must flea from danger, too. _____

2. If you are near the ocean, move strait away from the rough waters.

 _____

3. People should warn each other as soon as a storm is in site.

 _____

4. Once I saw a storm make a flag poll look like it was falling down.

 _____

5. The flag flew in the breeze as fast as I have ever scene. _____

6. There whir fallen tree branches where I was standing. _____

7. Many storms can be a reel danger if people are not careful. _____

8. The boys will stay off the pier until the boat is hear. _____

9. "It is never a waste to warn someone about the whether," says Mom.

 _____

Confusing Words!

Complete each sentence. Circle the correct word in parentheses.
Use a dictionary if you are unsure of which word is correct.

1. The sunset had a calming _____ on the water. (affect / effect)

2. In his magic show, Leo the Great tricked us with an amazing _____.
(allusion / illusion)

3. We think offering juice instead of soda is a great _____.
(alternate / alternative)

4. The rest stop is just a few miles _____ down the road. (farther / further)

5. Your _____ sent home a note today about the class trip.
(principle / principal)

6. Mom wanted to know _____ boots were by the
kitchen door. (who's / whose)

7. I cannot explain _____ shape and size without
saying really big! (it's / its)

8. Some important decisions were made in the _____
building that day. (capital / capitol)

9. My friend will always stand _____ me through
thick and thin. (beside / besides)

10. We can write Grandma a letter on my new _____.
(stationary / stationery)

Predicates and More Predicates

A **compound predicate** is more than one predicate with the same subject. The words *and* and *or* are often used to connect predicates in a sentence.

For example:
I do homework during the week *and* play soccer on the weekends.
My brother will help to do my homework *or* kick a ball around.

Read each sentence. Underline each predicate and
circle the word that joins them to make a compound predicate.

1. My mom drives me to soccer practice and makes dinner afterwards.

2. We play for an hour and discuss our strategies.

3. Matt brings snacks and passes them out to us.

4. We rest on the bench and get ready to play again.

5. Coach talks to us and cheers us on.

6. Our friends sit in the stands and watch us play.

7. My mom sips her coffee and chats with the other parents.

8. Do you think I can be the team captain next year, or host the team party at my house?

Homophone and Homograph Fun

Remember: **Homophones** are words that sound alike but have different spellings and meanings. **Homographs** are words that have the same spelling but different meanings. Some homographs have different pronunciations.

Read each sentence. Write *homophone* or *homograph* to identify the underlined words.

1. The choir had to sing the <u>hymn</u> again for <u>him</u>. _____

2. Debra will <u>present</u> the <u>present</u> to our teacher right after lunch. _____

3. Jorge was getting <u>hoarse</u> calling after the new <u>horse</u> at the farm. _____

4. Dad got a <u>pain</u> in his back putting in a new <u>pane</u> for the living room window. _____

5. I always <u>spring</u> into action and clean the garage once the <u>spring</u> comes.

_____

Complete each sentence. Circle the correct homophone in parentheses.

6. I think our team is getting good enough to _____ our opponents. (beat / beet)

7. I heard the bird _____ this morning as I was waking up. (cheap / cheep)

8. The sandpaper felt _____ when she touched it. (coarse / course)

9. Each morning there is _____ on the front lawn. (do / dew)

10. Every _____ we have a math test in class. (weak / week)

What Do You See Here?

Descriptive writing uses details to tell about something. You can use a picture to practice your descriptive writing.

Write a story about the picture you see below. Make up details about the characters and what you see. Include as many details as you can.

_____

_____

_____

_____

_____

_____

_____

_____

May I Persuade You?

A **persuasive letter** is written to convince one or more people to agree with your viewpoint. Like any letter, it has an opening and closing.

People say that children need exercise every day.
What do you think of that idea? Write a letter to your doctor
explaining your position. Try to convince him or her to agree with you.

_____

_____

_____

_____

_____

_____

_____

_____

_____

_____

In the Middle of It All

Remember: A good story has a **beginning**, a **middle**, and an **end**. In the middle of the story, the focus is on the problem, or **conflict**.

Write a middle part for the story below.

As soon as Shantelle got to school, she put her book bag on her desk. "All right everyone," said her teacher. "Take out your homework assignments." A look of terror came over Shantelle's face.

_____

_____

_____

_____

_____

_____

_____

_____

_____

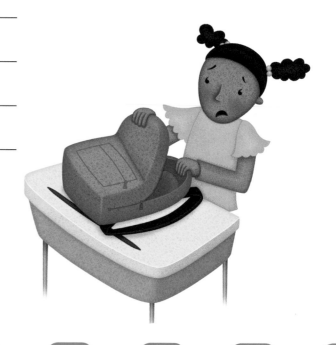

Shantelle sat back down in her seat, relieved that her problem had been solved. She wondered what her teacher would be assigning for homework tonight.

It's All About the Order

Sequence is the order in which events happen. When reading, pay attention to the sequence of events. This will help you to understand the story better.

Number the events below in the correct order.

_____ Relieved, Jessie waved at the cheering crowd during his last curtain call. "It was definitely worth the effort," he said to himself.

_____ Jessie finally felt comfortable with his lines and he shut his bedroom light. "Time to get some sleep," he thought to himself.

_____ "You don't even know your lines yet," said Jessie's mom. "The play is tomorrow. Now go to your room and start studying!"

_____ The next day, Jessie had butterflies in his stomach as he stood on the stage. The curtain went up and he delivered his first line with courage.

_____ Jessie slammed the door of his room. He was nervous about the play. He had tried to memorize his lines, but he was having so much trouble that he gave up for a while. Now he had no choice but to study.

Savvy Summarizing

When you **summarize** what you read, you use your own words to tell about it. A summary gives the most important information.

Write a summary of the story below.

Monica looked out over the ocean. She had seen the sunset over the shoreline so many times before, but tonight it all looked different. She was seeing everything with her new pair of eyeglasses. It was the most beautiful sunset she had seen in a long time.

Monica was having trouble seeing for months, but she could not put her finger on what the problem was. She used to get headaches during class, and she could not read what her teacher was writing on the board. She didn't think that any of this had to do with her vision until she went to the school nurse for a routine eye exam.

Monica's mother took her to an eye doctor for a full exam, and they fitted her for her first pair of glasses. Monica didn't like the idea at first, but when she put the glasses on, she was shocked at how well she could see everything.

"Wow!" she said. "I think I've been missing a lot!"

Is It a Sentence?

A **complete sentence** is a group of words that expresses a complete idea or thought. It also starts with a capital letter and ends in a period, exclamation point, or question mark.

Read each sentence. Write whether it is *complete* or *incomplete.* If it is a complete sentence, rewrite it so it has correct capitalization and punctuation.

1. we can't begin the game until Sara gets here _____

_____

2. would be late _____

_____

3. the game four people to play _____

_____

4. she has always been the best player, so it makes sense to wait for her

_____

5. Look, here she is now _____

_____

6. can we start the game soon _____

_____

Subjects and Predicates

A **subject** is the person, place, or thing that a sentence is about.
The **predicate** is the part of a sentence with a verb. It tells about the
subject is doing or describes its state of being.

For example: <u>My dog</u>   <u>likes to run along the beach</u>.
                  subject   **predicate**

Read each sentence. Write whether the underlined part is the *subject* or the *predicate*.

1. <u>Pedro's birthday</u> is coming up soon. _____

2. Mom <u>looked carefully at his birthday list</u>. _____

3. She <u>thinks it is time for Pedro to get a new bike</u>. _____

4. <u>Mom, Dad, Carlos, and I</u> went shopping for the bike last night. _____

5. <u>I</u> think Pedro will be very happy. _____

Read each sentence. Circle the subject and underline the predicate.

6. My bike is brand-new.

7. I got it from my family for my birthday.

8. Aunt Tabitha and Uncle Cameron got me
a bicycle pump and a helmet.

9. Lincoln Park and Willow Court are my
favorite places to bike.

10. Now my sister wants a new bike, too.

Why So Wordy?

When writing, it makes sense to look back at what you have written to see if you can make your sentences less **wordy**. Think about ways to say the same thing in a clearer way by using fewer words.

For example:

Wordy   She thinks the car that belongs to her mom is low on gas.
Better   She thinks her mom's car is low on gas.

Rewrite the paragraph so that the underlined parts are less wordy.

    I have been doing my own laundry for a few months. First, I wait until a pile of clothes collects in my <u>bin that is meant just for collecting dirty clothes</u>. Then I separate the clothes by <u>dark, light, colorful, and any other categories that have to do with color that will help me do the wash</u>. After that, I put one pile of clothes into the washing machine with a half capful of <u>the liquid that is meant to wash clothing</u>. After the machine washes the clothes, I <u>take each piece of clothing out of one machine and put it in the dryer</u>. Soon, I've got fresh, clean clothes again.

_____

_____

_____

_____

Puzzling Prepositions

A **preposition** is a word that shows the relation between a noun or pronoun and the rest of the sentence. Words like *in, on, below, at,* and *without* are examples of prepositions. A **prepositional phrase** is made up of a preposition and the phrase that it describes.

For example:
  The dog is *in the bathtub.*
  In is the preposition. The prepositional phrase is *in the bathtub.*

Read each sentence. Circle the preposition and underline the prepositional phrase.

1. Dad's wallet is on the counter.

2. He wants you to grab it so we can go to the store.

3. Mom says there is almost nothing in the refrigerator.

4. I know we've gone without strawberry milk for long enough.

5. There's a shopping list by Mom's purse.

6. She says we must check it before we go through the checkout line.

7. I'll bet Mom can't wait until we get home and bring the groceries inside.

8. I wonder what we will have after dinner.

9. I can almost smell the chicken soup on the stove.

10. Hopefully there will also be an apple pie in the oven.

Shopping List

1. straw-berry Milk
2. chicken
3. carrots
4. celery
5. pasta
6. apples
7. pie crust

Proofread It!

When you **proofread**, you read what you have written to try to find errors.
Look for errors in punctuation, spelling, and grammar.

Read each sentence carefully to look for errors. Rewrite each sentence so that it is correct.

1. I wish I coulds bake the pumpkin Pie with you.

_____

2. Will you saved a piece for me when you are finished.

_____

3. The Best place to get the Pie is at Leos Markets'.

_____

4. yous must by the best ingredients to put in to the pye.

_____

Read the paragraph carefully. Rewrite the paragraph to fix any errors you see.

I could not believes my eye. I saw a family of Raccoons crawl into the sewer near our home "They must live there", I thought to myself? Why else would they all go down there together! my brother wanted to shines a flashlight down there two see them. "No Way," my mom said? "leave that poor family alone

_____

_____

_____

_____

_____

Choose Carefully...or Careful?

What is the difference between an adverb and an adjective? An **adjective** describes a noun, while **adverbs** describe verbs, adjectives, other adverbs, or other parts of a sentence. Adverbs often end in *-ly*.

For example:
Adverb: The boy *ran quickly*.   (*Quickly* describes a verb.)
Adjective: Listen to my *quick* answer.   (*Quick* describes a noun.)

Complete each sentence. Circle the correct word in parentheses.
Then underline the word that the adverb or adjective describes.

1. Jen is (lucky / luckily) to have me as a sister.

2. She has (near / nearly) finished painting her room.

3. We worked (quick / quickly) together to get the job done.

4. We were (hysterical / hysterically) over her choice of paint colors.

5. She had a (ridiculous / ridiculously) idea to make polka dots all over the walls.

6. We had to (careful / carefully) draw perfect circles on the walls and then paint them in.

7. Mom was impressed at our (diligent / diligently) work together.

8. We must have painted a hundred (round / roundly) circles in an hour.

9. Now we have to wait (patient / patiently) for the walls to dry.

10. The next step will be to decorate the room (imaginative / imaginatively).

Different Pronouns

A **subject pronoun** takes the place of a subject in a sentence. Subject pronouns are *I, we, they, you, he, she,* and *it.* **Object pronouns** take the place of objects in a sentence. Object pronouns are *me, us, them, you, him, her,* and *it.*

For example:

Subject pronoun	*They* are my best friends.
Object pronoun	Those kids really like *us*.

Complete each sentence. Circle the correct pronoun in parentheses.

1. _____ feed my goldfish everyday. (I / Me)

2. Who wants to feed _____ while I'm away? (him / he)

3. _____ lives in a tank in the living room. (Them / He)

4. _____ takes only a minute to pour some flakes into the tank. (It / Them)

5. Who do you think should feed _____? (his / him)

6. _____ don't want him to be hungry. (I / Me)

Write *subject pronoun* or *object pronoun* to identify each underlined word.

7. Dad bought <u>me</u> the fish for my birthday last year. _____

8. <u>It</u>'s my favorite gift. _____

Suave Summarizing

Remember: When you **summarize**, you tell the most important information in your own words. It helps to summarize nonfiction information because it may help you to remember the facts better.

Read the following passage and answer the questions below.

An Internet search engine can help you quickly find what you are looking for on the Internet. A search engine such as Google.com has a search field for you to type in what you are looking for. Be sure to use keywords that are as exact as possible. Put words in quotation marks to help you narrow down your search. Simply type the words into the search screen and press the search button.

You will be given a list of all of the Web sites that match your search. Your search may come up with many results, but you will only see the first 20 or so on your computer screen. If you see a Web site listing that you would like to investigate or look at, simply click on the underlined link to be brought to that Web page.

1. Write a summary of the passage.

_____

_____

_____

_____

2. What were some details that you did not feel were important to put in your summary?

_____

_____

_____

_____

Conclusion Solution

Remember: **Sequence** is the order of events. When we sequence information, we put it in the order of events that occurred or steps that must be taken.

Read the following passage and answer the questions below.

Paul Revere played an important role as a patriot during the American Revolution. His job was to deliver information to Massachusetts colonists about the war. On April 18, 1775, Revere rode his famous "Midnight Ride."

After two lights were lit in the tower of the Old North Church that night, Revere took off on his journey. The two lights were meant to warn colonists that British soldiers were coming by sea. One if by land, two if by sea, the saying went.

Revere started by crossing the Charles River by boat and mounting a horse that was waiting for him on the other side. He rode through the night on his way from Boston to Lexington. He called out along the way to warn colonists that the British were coming. Revere's ride was successful.

Paul Revere's actions did not become famous until 40 years after he died and Henry Wadsworth Longfellow wrote the poem "Paul Revere's Ride."

1. When did Paul Revere make his Midnight Ride?

_____

2. What happened in Boston before Revere started his journey?

_____

3. What was the first thing Paul Revere did to start his trip?

_____

4. When did Paul Revere's ride become famous?

_____

How Do You Do That?

Remember: **How-to writing** tells people how to do things. Recipes, directions, and owner's manuals are examples of how-to writing.

Think of something you know how to do well.
Write directions for someone, explaining how to do it.

_____

_____

_____

_____

_____

_____

_____

_____

Tell Me All About It

Plot describes the events of a story. A plot includes a story's problem, or conflict. The events in a plot happen in an order that makes sense to the reader.

For example:

In the plot of "Goldilocks and the Three Bears," a young girl explores the bear family's home while they are out for a walk.

Think of your favorite story. Explain the plot of the story in detail.

_____

_____

_____

_____

_____

_____

_____

_____

Subject and Verb Agreement

The subject and verb of a sentence must agree in number. **Singular verbs** are used with singular subjects. **Plural verbs** are used with plural subjects.

For example:

Singular   *Abby sings* a solo at the concert.
Plural   *The girls sing* right after Abby does.

Complete each sentence. Circle the correct verb in parentheses to agree with the subject of the sentence.

1. We (invite / invites) Raj to help us make a tree house.

2. He (know / knows) a lot about building things.

3. Minnie (say / says) Raj can build anything he sets his mind to.

4. Davis and Leon (buy / buys) the materials to build the tree house.

5. This store (sell / sells) wood for less than that store.

Circle any verb that does not show agreement in the paragraph below.

6. Jacob and Lily loves to cook. They makes a meal for their friends every weekend. Sometimes, the meals is very simple. Other times the recipes are very complicated. Next week, they will make a spicy shrimp gumbo. We loves to eat with them whenever they cook!

What a Description!

When writing a descriptive paragraph, think about words that will help you be as clear as possible. **Descriptive adjectives** help give the reader information about your topic.

Think about what an apple looks, tastes, smells, and feels like. Then write a paragraph to describe an apple. Use as many descriptive adjectives as possible.

_____

_____

_____

_____

_____

_____

_____

_____

_____

_____

How Can I Persuade You?

Remember: Some writing is meant to **persuade**, or convince, the reader of something. Persuasive writing often uses opinions to make the reader believe or understand something.

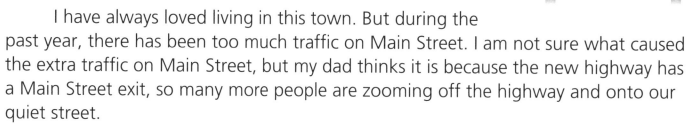

Read the letter and answer the questions below.

Dear Mayor,

    I have always loved living in this town. But during the past year, there has been too much traffic on Main Street. I am not sure what caused the extra traffic on Main Street, but my dad thinks it is because the new highway has a Main Street exit, so many more people are zooming off the highway and onto our quiet street.

    I suggest that you make a back road to keep the cars that come off the highway from suddenly getting slowed down on our street. Most of them want to pass through quickly to get to Mall Turnpike, so it makes sense to make a road that allows cars to avoid Main Street.

    Thanks for taking the time to think about this problem.

    Sincerely,
    Rita Leopold

1. What is the problem that the author points out to the mayor?

_____

_____

2. What is the author trying to persuade the mayor to do?

_____

_____

3. Why does the author think her solution will work?

_____

_____

Compare and Contrast the Facts

Remember: **Comparing** means telling how things are alike.
Contrasting means telling how things are different.

Compare and contrast baseball and football, based on the passage below.

It is unclear when the first game of baseball was played in the United States, but it is thought to have started during the 1800s. The basic rules of baseball have remained constant over the years. Each time a player makes it around the bases after hitting a ball with a wooden bat, a point is scored. There are normally nine innings in a baseball game. Today there are two organizations in major league baseball that play each other each season until one championship team remains: the National League and the American League.

American football can be traced back to the 1890s. The rules started out similar to soccer and rugby. Like these sports, each football team tries to throw or kick the ball past the opposing team's end zone within a given amount of time. Over the years, however, the sport has changed to the one we know today. There is one organization today for professional football: the National Football League.

1. Name three ways baseball and football are alike.

_____

_____

_____

2. Name three ways baseball and football are different.

_____

_____

_____

Puzzling Titles

The titles of books, magazines, newspapers, TV shows, and movies are written in italics. The titles of songs, articles, stories, poems, or essays are written in quotation marks. Capitalize all important words of a title, including the first and last word.

For example:
  The Wizard of Oz (movie and book)   "The Three Bears" (story)
  Chicago Sun-Times (newspaper)   "Humpty Dumpty" (poem)

Read each title. Write *correct* if the title is written correctly.
Write *incorrect* if it is written incorrectly.

1. "The new york times" (newspaper) _____

2. "My Native Country" (essay) _____

3. *Hoot* (book) _____

4. *Why I love ice cream so much* (article) _____

5. "National Geographic kids" (magazine) _____

6. "oh the places you'll go!" (book) _____

7. *The Miami Herald* (newspaper) _____

8. "Hannah Montana" (TV show) _____

9. *My Best Friend Is a Monkey* (movie) _____

A Trip for Two

An **antecedent** is a noun or group of nouns that a pronoun refers to.
A pronoun must agree with its antecedent in number and gender.

For example:
Antecedent   <u>Gary and Alexa</u> play the violin.
Pronoun   <u>They</u> practice every day.

Read each sentence. Circle the antecedent for each underlined word.

1. The squirrel quickly scampered up the tree. <u>It</u> must have been in a hurry.

2. Olivia chased the squirrel as fast as <u>she</u> could.

3. Maya laughed at Olivia. It seems <u>she</u> is always laughing at Olivia.

4. Dad and I chased after Olivia. <u>We</u> knew she would forget about that squirrel soon.

5. Then we went home. Our house is not as interesting as the park, but <u>it</u> has fewer surprises for Olivia.

Complete each sentence. Write the correct pronoun. Then circle the antecedent.

6. Jenna wished she could play the piano. _____ wanted to start lessons soon.

7. "But we don't have a piano at home," said Mom. _____ definitely had a good point.

8. Jenna decided to switch to the guitar and use her dad's. "I know _____ won't mind," she said.

9. "I guess you are right about the guitar," said Mom. "Dad won't mind if you borrow _____."

Alike or Different?

Good writers sometimes **compare** and **contrast** things in their writing. A Venn diagram helps a writer compare and contrast.

Use the Venn diagram below to compare and contrast two
of your favorite foods. Then use the information to write a paragraph.

Making It Happen

Remember: In writing, a **cause** makes something happen. An **effect** is what happens as a result.

Read the cause below. Then finish the story by writing an effect.

Ben took swimming classes for months. He worked very hard and tried his best to keep going, even when he felt tired and frustrated.

_____

_____

_____

_____

_____

_____

_____

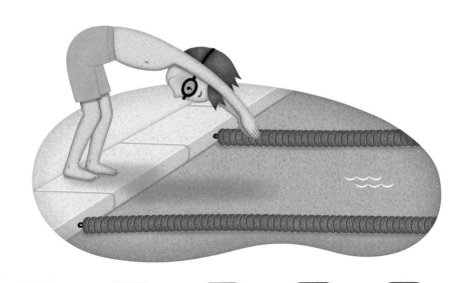

Crazy Conjunctions

> A **conjunction** joins words or phrases together. The words *and, but, yet, for, so,* and *or* are conjunctions.

Read each sentence. Underline the conjunction.

1. My brother is an athlete, and I am a scholar.

2. He likes to play sports but doesn't always want to do his homework.

3. I would be happy either playing a game or reading a book.

4. I think learning can be a lot of work, yet I really enjoy it.

5. For the most part I enjoy sports, too, so I guess I'm a happy student.

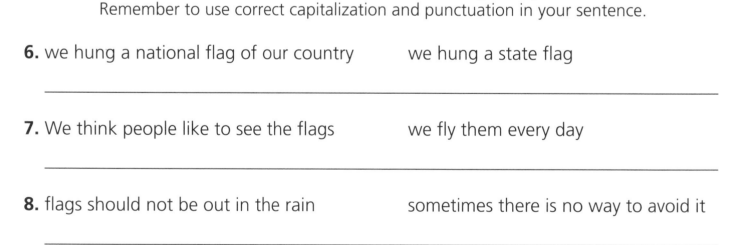

Combine the phrases into one sentence using a conjunction.
Remember to use correct capitalization and punctuation in your sentence.

6. we hung a national flag of our country   we hung a state flag

_____

7. We think people like to see the flags   we fly them every day

_____

8. flags should not be out in the rain   sometimes there is no way to avoid it

_____

What a Description!

A **run-on sentence** joins two independent clauses without punctuation or conjunctions. To avoid run-on sentences, use a comma or conjunction to join the two clauses. You may also turn a run-on sentence into two sentences.

For example:

Run-on   My salad looks delicious I don't have time to eat it.
Correct   My salad looks delicious, but I don't have time to eat it.

Rewrite each run-on sentence as one compound sentence.

1. My favorite restaurant is Louie's we know the owner.

_____

2. I love their soups and salads they always have very prompt service.

_____

3. We went there last week for Gina's birthday she had a great time.

_____

Rewrite each run-on sentence as two simple sentences.

4. My sister thinks she wants to be a chef she goes to Louie's to taste new foods.

_____

5. She wishes that Louie would give her recipes he keeps them secret from everyone.

_____

6. I wish I knew how to make Louie's vegetable soup it is the best in the world.

_____

Plan It Out

When writing a fiction story, good writers **plan** what they are going to write about. A graphic organizer can help you record your thoughts before you begin to write your essay.

Think of a fiction story you would like to write about. Write the main idea in the center oval of the concept map below. Then put details in the surrounding ovals. Write your story on a separate sheet of paper.

Listen to My Story

Narrative writing tells a story or a part of a story. It can be written from the point of view of the author or from another viewpoint.

For example:

> I dipped my toe into the cold water of the pool and pulled it back again quickly. It was too cold for me! I sat back on the lounge chair and opened my magazine. Maybe the water will be a little warmer this afternoon.

Write a narrative from a dog's viewpoint.

_____

_____

_____

_____

_____

_____

_____

Explain It to Me

Expository writing gives information that explains, defines, or instructs. It uses supporting details, descriptive language, and a logical order. Most expository writing is nonfiction.

For example:

> If you see an object moving across the night sky, you may very well be looking at a comet. A comet is an icy body that has a trail of debris behind it. The trail is what helps many people tell the comet from an asteroid in the sky.

Choose a topic you would like to write about. Do any research necessary and write an expository paragraph about the topic.

_____

_____

_____

_____

_____

_____

_____

Where and When

The **setting** of a story is the time and place in which the story happens. A story's setting can be in the past, present, or future. It can take place anywhere.

Write a story that takes place in the future.
Include detailed information about the setting of your story.

_____

_____

_____

_____

_____

_____

_____

_____

_____

Conclusions, Conclusions

Remember: When you **draw a conclusion**, you use what you know and what you have read to make a decision about something.

Draw conclusions based on the passage to answer the questions below.

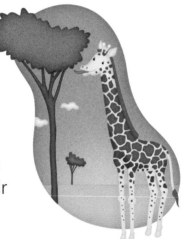

Giraffes are the tallest land animals on earth. They can grow to be up to 18 feet tall and weigh almost two tons. The most interesting feature of the giraffe is its long neck. The animal uses its long neck to reach leaves on tree branches. Most other animals cannot reach food this high in trees. This gives giraffes an advantage because they do not have to compete as much for their food. Giraffes live in southern Africa where the climate is warm and there are many grasslands and savannas.

1. Why would a giraffe survive better in southern Africa rather than a cold place where trees lose their leaves in winter?

_____

2. What might happen if another animal with a long neck lived on the savanna with the giraffe?

_____

3. Give an example of another animal adaptation.

_____

4. What other conclusion can you draw about giraffes?

_____

_____

_____

Causes and Effects

Remember: A **cause** is a reason something happens. An **effect** is something that happens as a result of something else. Sometimes one effect can have several causes.

Read the passage. Then answer the questions below.

What causes floods to occur? It's not just rain. When heavy snows melt quickly, the ground may not have the time to absorb all the water. As a result, the water collects on the ground. Sometimes it flows downhill and collects at the bottom of a hill or mountain.

Another cause of floods is when heavy rains happen more quickly than the ground can soak up the water. Other floods are caused when river waters rise over their banks and onto the land.

Floods can have devastating effects. Property damage and loss of human life are big problems in dangerous floods. Other effects include loss of wildlife habitats.

1. What are two causes of floods?

_____

_____

2. What are two effects of floods?

_____

_____

3. What do you think a cause and effect of a drought might be?

Cause: _____

Effect: _____

Interview Someone You Know

Reporting is one form of writing. Reporters for newspapers often interview people to get first hand information. An interview is a session of questions and answers about a topic.

Write interview questions for a person you know. Then ask the person the questions to learn more about his or her interests and hobbies. Record the answers.

Question: _____

_____

Answer: _____

_____

Question: _____

_____

Answer: _____

_____

Question: _____

_____

Answer: _____

_____

_____

Writing from an Interview

After a writer has interviewed someone, the interview can be turned into a piece of writing, such as an article or story.

Use the interview you conducted for the previous exercise to write a short article about the person you interviewed.

_____

_____

_____

_____

_____

_____

_____

_____

_____

_____

_____

_____

_____

Good Description!

Remember: In **descriptive writing**, adjectives help give the reader information about your topic. They can also help make your writing more interesting.

Think about an emotion you have felt before. Describe what you felt.
Use as many descriptive adjectives as possible.

_____

_____

_____

_____

_____

_____

_____

_____

Viewpoint Views

In persuasive writing, an author presents a **viewpoint** and tries to convice the reader to support it.

Think about what your own viewpoint is as you read the following passage. Then answer the questions below.

Recycling is very important. If we did not recycle, our landfills would be even more filled than they already are and our planet would be covered in garbage. However, recycling can be costly and difficult to coordinate. People must be trusted to do their part to recycle properly. When mistakes are made, valuable time, money, and resources are wasted.

The most important thing people can do to help the environment is to use fewer resources in the first place. If we used fewer resources, we would not have such a waste problem. Food, toy, and other product packaging can be made with less cardboard and plastic. Reusing resources such as bags, containers, and paper are also smart ways to use less. Think about what you use each day and then think about how you can use less of it. To truly make a difference, we must all work together.

1. What is the author's viewpoint about the importance of recycling?

_____

_____

2. What is the author's viewpoint about what we can do for the environment?

_____

_____

3. What is your viewpoint about the subject?

_____

_____

Brainstorm!

A good writer will **brainstorm** a list of writing ideas before choosing the best one.

For example:

Possible story ideas: rainy days, snow days, first day of school, best friends, favorite band, favorite food, favorite animal, trip to zoo, birthday party for friend

Brainstorm a list of story ideas on the left side of the page. Then choose one of the story ideas from the list and brainstorm about it on the right side of the page. Include your ideas about the story's setting, characters, and plot.

_____   _____

_____   _____

_____   _____

_____   _____

_____   _____

_____   _____

_____   _____

_____   _____

Ready! Set! Write!

Use the brainstorming notes from page 88 to write a story.

_____

_____

_____

_____

_____

_____

_____

_____

_____

_____

_____

_____

Any Questions?

Prewriting is a stage of writing in which the writer records important information. One way to prewrite is to record *who, what, when, where,* and *why*.

Choose a topic. Fill in the chart with the information about the topic. Then use the information to write a short paragraph.

Who	
What	
When	
Where	
Why	

A Revision Vision

When you **revise** writing, you fix errors and make improvements. A revision can fix errors in spelling, punctuation, and grammar. It can also change sentences in a draft to make them sound better.

Read the draft below. Write a revision in the space provided.
Fix errors and try to make the text read better.

A Dalmatian is the best kind in the world. It is the only dog with black and white spots. Dalmatian puppys are borne with fur that is all white, and they shed that fur and grow fir with spots on it. Mail dalmations are usually bigger then females. Dalmatians are fast runnerz and has lota energy. and they need a many of exersise. By the way, dalmatians are dogs.

_____

_____

_____

_____

_____

_____

_____

Answer Key

Page 4
1. dis-
2. re-
3. non-
4. re-
5. trans-
6. c
7. b
8. a
9. d

Page 5
1. -ful
2. -ly
3. -ness
4. -able
5. -ly
6. b
7. d
8. e
9. a
10. c

Page 6
1. My little sister, Lanie, loves superheroes like Batman and Spider Man.
2. She bought a superhero coloring book when we visited San Diego, California.
3. We were there for Thanksgiving last year and walked along Main Street.
4. Lanie pointed and cheered at every superhero poster outside Lowland Theaters.
5. Mom and Dad bought her a Green Lantern action figure.
6. They gave it to her for her birthday in December.
7. When she opened it, she thought it was the best gift in the world!

Page 7
1. present
2. future
3. future
4. present
5. past
6. present
7. past
8. future
9. past
10. past

Page 8
1. shirt
2. protest
3. tired
4. loyal
5. giant
6. remark
7. conference
8. fierce
9. national

Page 9
1. boring
2. plain
3. casual
4. upset
5. inattentive
6. clean
7. leave
8. encouraged
9. love
10. impatient

Page 10
1. fact
2. fact
3. fact
4. opinion
5. opinion
6. opinion

Page 11
Descriptions will vary.

Page 12
1. communicate
2. found
3. change
4. illustrate
5. introduce
6. coward
7. disturb
8. approve
9. assist
10. economy
11. intelligent
12. similar
13. responsible
14. serious

Page 13
1. c
2. e
3. b
4. a
5. d

6. h
7. i
8. g
9. j
10. f

Page 14
1. We left our toothbrushes on the sink and put on our pajamas.
2. My dog ate cookies and biscuits off the floor.
3. The students put their backpacks on the floor and hung up their coats.
4. I saw so many fish in the ocean today!
5. I returned my books to the library today.
6. We ran through the streets as quickly as we could.
7. I met my classmate on the playground today.
8. Mom saw the snowmen we made in the yard.

Page 15
1. The dog's bone is in the backyard.
2. Sue's brother is at the door.
3. The dog's blanket is in the dryer.
4. The house's color is blue.
5. Samantha's friend is sick today.
6. Jenny's necklace is beautiful.
7. The bird's nest was hidden in the branches.

Page 16
1. sing
2. runs
3. join
4. love
5. try
6. boys
7. dog
8. He
9. boys
10. know

Page 17
Story endings will vary.

Page 18
Character descriptions will vary.

Page 19
Facts: The elephant uses its trunk to tear branches from trees and then to place the branch into its mouth to eat The trunk is used for drinking, too. Elephants suck water into their trunks and then blow it into their mouths to drink! The trunk is even used to greet other elephants.

Opinions: The elephant is one of the most interesting animals in the world. When people think of the elephant, they often wish they could learn more about it. The animal's best feature is its trunk. Many people think that two elephants greeting each other with their trunks looks a little like two people shaking hands.

Page 20
Main idea: Jake is a great baseball player and wants to be a professional one day.

Supporting details: Jake loved seeing a game when he was little. He started practicing after that day. When he was old enough for a team, he was already the best player.

Page 21
Sentences will vary.
1. unbalanced
2. nonsense
3. misunderstand
4. reassure
5. unbelievable
6. preview
7. postseason
8. unimportant
9. relive

Page 22
Sentences will vary.
1. wonderful
2. conductor
3. brighten
4. sincerely
5. placement
6. scientist
7. fearful
8. fearless
9. quickly

Page 23

"Hurry up," said Dad. "The bus is going to be here any minute!"

"OK," I yelled back. I quickly looked around the room. I could not find my backpack anywhere. "I'll be there in a minute!" I said.

"What's taking you so long?" Dad said, standing in the doorway with my backpack in his hands. "It looks like you lost something."

"Dad!" I said. "I was looking for that! Thanks."

Page 24

1. Jerry does not think anybody will come to his party.
2. He doesn't have any friends.
3. He hasn't lived in town for a very long time.
4. His mom told him he couldn't invite anybody who was a stranger.
5. Jerry can't ever wait for a birthday, even if very few people come to his party.
6. Nobody makes cake better than Aunt Carmen.
7. Jerry doesn't have anything to worry about.

Page 25

1. yellow
2. huge
3. remarkable
4. furry
5. twelve
6. hilarious
7. difficult
8. soft
9. adorable

Page 26

1. They'll
2. We'd
3. couldn't
4. aren't
5. shouldn't
6. I'll
7. It's
8. We'll
9. He'd
10. We're

Page 27

Story beginnings will vary.

Page 28

Friendly letters will vary.

Page 29

1. science fiction

2. The story takes place in the future and we can see influences of science and technology on the story.
3. There was technology in the story that we do not have today, such as homes on autopilot and vehicles that deliver pizza from space stations.

Page 30

1. drain out the water
2. a six-ounce can
3. a small amount of low-fat mayonnaise and possibly celery
4. cut the sandwich in half

Page 31

1. Who has a better teacher, Alex or Alyssa?
2. "That's not a fair question," said Marcus. "People like teachers for different reasons," he said.
3. "I know the answer!" said Alyssa. "I definitely have the better teacher because we hardly get any homework at all."
4. "Well, I think my teacher is better," said Alex. "She might give us a lot of homework, but we all learn a lot from her every day."
5. Only one of the teachers gives homework in social studies, math, english, and science every night.
6. Does that make her a good teacher or a bad teacher?

Page 32

1. The best essay in the class was hers.
2. The teacher read the essay that was theirs.
3. I cannot understand the essay that is yours.
4. Do you like the essay that is mine?
5. My
6. Our
7. my

Page 33

1. I love it when the winter sky gets cold, gray, and cloudy.
2. It has been snowing all day, and soon I will be able to make a snowman.

3. First, I check for clothes that I can wear outside in the snow.
4. I find a hat, mittens, a scarf, boots, and a coat.
5. Next, I eat a good lunch so I have the energy to make my snowman.
6. I gather snow, pack it, and roll it across the yard.
7. Suddenly, I get a little discouraged because I realize I cannot lift the snowballs.
8. That's when Dad comes out, and he is ready to help me.
9. I am happy that he helps, but then he makes me help clear snow off the car, driveway, stairs, and walkway.
10. As I shovel, my snowman watches me, and I think he may have winked at me!

Page 34

1. We will hand out the athletes' uniforms.
2. I will keep track of both teams' points.
3. The coaches' tips help the teams do well.
4. The children's efforts are outstanding.
5. I can hear the fans' cheers!
6. May I see the animals' homes?
7. The farmers brought us to the chicken's nest.

Page 35

Possible answers:
1. beautiful; ugly
2. expand; shrink
3. run; walk
4. rebel; obey
5. defend; harm
6. sleepy; alert
7. quickly; slowly
8. catch; throw
9. serious; minor
10. help; hurt

Page 36

1. garbage or litter
2. to be disloyal
3. respect
4. inexperienced person
5. his parents died when he was three; example
6. demands; definition
7. many rabbits eating in the garden; example

Page 37

1. unhappiness
2. misleading
3. impatiently
4. improperly
5. previewing
6. one who
7. state or condition of
8. three
9. not
10. before

Page 38

1. simile
2. metaphor
3. metaphor
4. simile
5. simile
6. simile
7. simile

Page 39

Main idea: The hobbyhorse was an invention that looked like an early bicycle, but was used for walking.

Supporting details: Baron von Drais invented the hobbyhorse in 1817. It was made out of wood and became popular in the 1800s. It could only be used to walk with, not ride on.

Page 40

Me: long brown hair, likes to watch comedies

Both

Sara: short blond hair, likes to watch dramas

friends, same grade, on swim team, do homework before swimming

Page 41

1. She will ask Mrs. Donnelley if she can rake her leaves for money.
2. a rake, garbage bags
3. She needs more money to buy a present for her parents, and Mrs. Donnelley is very busy.

Page 42

Cause	Effect
1. The weather report is given.	People decide to leave their homes.
2. We live near the beach and are used to storms.	Dad and I board up the house again.
3. We have a strong house.	We feel confident that our house will be okay.

Page 43
Answers will vary.

Page 44
Answers will vary.

Page 45
Answers will vary.

Page 46
1. was
2. were
3. were
4. were
5. was
6. are
7. is; am
8. is
9. are
10. am

Page 47
1. independent
2. independent
3. dependent
4. dependent
5. independent
6. independent
7. dependent
8. independent
9. dependent

Page 48
1. flee
2. straight
3. sight
4. pole
5. seen
6. were
7. real
8. here
9. weather

Page 49
1. effect
2. illusion
3. alternative
4. farther
5. principal
6. whose
7. its
8. capitol
9. beside
10. stationery

Page 50
1. My mom drives me to soccer practice (and) makes dinner afterwards.
2. We play for a half hour (and) discuss our strategies.
3. Matt brings snacks (and) passes them out to us.
4. We rest on the bench (and) get ready to play again.
5. Coach talks to us (and) cheers us on.
6. Our friends sit in the stands (and) watch us play.
7. My mom sips her coffee (and) chats with the other parents.
8. Do you think I can be the team captain next year, (or) host the team party at my house?

Page 51
1. homophone
2. homograph
3. homophone
4. homophone
5. homograph
6. beat
7. cheep
8. coarse
9. dew
10. week

Page 52
Stories will vary.

Page 53
Persuasive letters will vary.

Page 54
Story middles will vary.

Page 55
Set: 5, 3, 1, 4, 2

Page 56
Summaries may vary but should include: Monica has her first pair of eyeglasses and can see everything better than she had before. She learned she needed glasses from having a routine eye exam with the school nurse. She then went to an eye doctor and was given a full exam and a pair of eyeglasses.

Page 57
1. complete
   We can't begin the game until Sara gets here.
2. incomplete
3. incomplete
4. complete
   She has always been the best player, so it makes sense to wait for her.
5. complete
   Look, here she is now!
6. complete
   Can we start the game soon?

Page 58
1. subject
2. predicate
3. predicate
4. subject
5. subject
6. (My bike) is brand new.
7. (I) got it from my family for my birthday.
8. (Aunt Tabitha and Uncle Cameron) got me a bicycle pump and a helmet.
9. (Lincoln Park and Willow Court) are my favorite places to bike.
10. Now (my sister) wants a new bike, too.

Page 59
I have been doing my own laundry for a few months. First, I wait until a pile of clothes collects in my hamper. Then I separate the clothes by color. After that, I put one pile of clothes into the washing machine with a half capful of detergent. After the machine washes the clothes, I move the clothes to the dryer. Soon, I've got fresh, clean clothes again.

Page 60
1. Dad's wallet is (on) the counter.
2. He wants you to grab it so we can go (to) the store.
3. Mom says there is almost nothing (in) the refrigerator.
4. I know we've gone (without) strawberry milk (for) long enough.
5. There's a shopping list (by) Mom's purse.
6. She says we must check it before we go (through) the checkout line.
7. I'll bet mom can't wait (until) we get home and bring the groceries inside.
8. I wonder what we will have (after) dinner.
9. I can almost smell the chicken soup (on) the stove.
10. Hopefully there will also be an apple pie (in) the oven.

Page 61
1. I wish I could bake the pumpkin pie with you.
2. Will you save a piece for me when you are finished?
3. The best place to get the pie is at Leo's Market.
4. You must buy the best ingredients to put into the pie.

I could not believe my eyes. I saw a family of raccoons crawl into the sewer near our home. "They must live there," I thought to myself. Why else would they all go down there together? My brother wanted to shine a flashlight down there to see them. "No way," my mom said. "Leave that poor family alone!"

Page 62
1. lucky; Jen
2. nearly; finished
3. quickly; worked
4. hysterical; we
5. ridiculous; idea
6. carefully; draw
7. diligent; work
8. round; circles
9. patiently; wait
10. imaginatively; decorate

Page 63
1. I
2. him
3. He
4. It
5. him
6. I
7. object pronoun
8. subject pronoun

Page 64
Answers will vary.

Page 65
1. April 18, 1775
2. Two lights were lit in the tower of the Old North Church.
3. He crossed the Charles River by boat.
4. A poem was written about it 40 years after he died.

Page 66
Answers will vary.

Page 67
Answers will vary.

Page 68
1. invite
2. knows
3. says
4. buy
5. sells
6. circle the words loves, makes, is, loves

Page 69
Answers will vary.

Page 70
1. The author points out that there is too much traffic on Main Street because of the new highway exit.
2. The author wants the mayor to build a back road that allows cars to avoid Main Street on their way to other places. The author thinks this will help the traffic problem on Main Street.
3. The author thinks her solution will work because she thinks most of the cars causing traffic on Main Street are going someplace else anyway.

Page 71
1. Both games date back to the 1800s. Both games have professional leagues today. Both games are played with a ball.
2. Baseball rules have remained constant over the years and football rules have not. There are two baseball organizations and only one football organization. In baseball, a ball his hit with a bat, and in football a ball can be kicked.

Page 72
1. incorrect
2. correct
3. correct
4. incorrect
5. incorrect
6. incorrect
7. correct
8. incorrect
9. correct

Page 73
1. squirrel
2. Olivia
3. Maya
4. Dad and I
5. our house
6. She / Jenna
7. She / Mom
8. he / her dad
9. it / guitar

Page 74
Answers will vary.

Page 75
Cause: Ben worked hard on his swimming. Effect: Answers will vary.

Page 76
1. and
2. but
3. or
4. yet
5. so
6. We hung a national flag and a state flag.
7. I think people like to see the flags, so we fly them every day.
8. Flags should not be out in the rain, but sometimes there is no way to avoid it.

Page 77
1. My favorite restaurant is Louie's and we know the owner.
2. I love their soups and salads, and they always have very prompt service.
3. We went there last week for Gina's birthday, and she had a great time.
4. My sister thinks she wants to be a chef. She goes to Louie's to taste new foods.
5. She wishes that Louie would give her recipes. He keeps them secret from everyone.
6. I wish I knew how to make Louie's vegetable soup. It is the best in the world.

Page 78
Concept maps will vary.

Page 79
Narratives will vary.

Page 80
Expository paragraphs will vary.

Page 81
Stories will vary.

Page 82
1. A giraffe relies on the leaves for food, so it would survive better where leaves are available all year long.
2. The giraffe might have less food because it would have to compete with the other animal.
3. Answers will vary, but might include the claws, wings, or beak of a bird because they can be used to fly or catch food.
4. Answers will vary, but might include that giraffes may weigh so much because they have many heavy bones to support their long necks and large bodies.

Page 83
1. rain, snowmelt, and overflowing rivers
2. property damage, loss of human life, and loss of wildlife habitats
3. Cause: the lack of rain for a long time. Effect: Plants and other living things in the ecosystem may not survive.

Page 84
Questions and answers will vary.

Page 85
Answers will vary.

Page 86
Descriptions will vary.

Page 87
1. Recycling is important, but perhaps not the most effective way to preserve our environment.
2. We can use fewer resources so that we have less waste to begin with.
3. Viewpoints will vary.

Page 88
Answers will vary.

Page 89
Answers will vary.

Page 90
Answers will vary.

Page 91
A Dalmatian is the best kind of dog in the world. It is the only dog with black and white spots. Dalmatian puppies are born with fur that is all white, and they shed that fur and grow fur with spots on it. Male Dalmatians are usually bigger than females. Dalmatians are fast runners and have a lot of energy. They need a lot of exercise.